Joke Book

Simon and Schuster
First published in Great Britain in 2013
by Simon and Schuster UK, Ltd
1st Floor, 222 Grays Inn Road,
London, WC1X 8HB
A CBS Company

ISBN: 978-1-4711-1774-9
Printed and bound in Great Britain
10 9 8 7 6 5 4 3 2 1
www.simonandschuster.co.uk
www.ZEPTOLAB.com

CUT the ROPE

Joke Book

h

Why did Om Nom paint himself in rainbow colours?

Because he wanted to hide in the crayon box.

What do you get if you cross Om Nom with a fountain pen?

The Ink-credible hulk.

What did Om Nom say when he met a lollipop?

Pleased to eat you.

Knock knock.
Who's there?
Ada.
Ada who?
Ada whole bag of candy!

What is dirty after Om Nom takes a bath?

The bathtub.

What do you call Om Nom when he has cotton wool in his ears?

Anything you like. He can't hear you.

Why did Om Nom
eat his homework?

Because the teacher told him
it was a piece of cake.

Why won't Om Nom tell
you the story about
peanut butter?

You might spread it.

What happened when Om Nom
crossed a cat and a parrot?

He got a carrot.

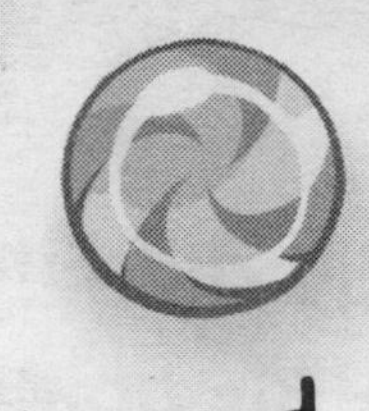

What are funny and taste good?

Candy jokes.

What country does candy come from?

Sweeten.

What's a ghost's favourite food?

I-scream.

Why did the spider buy a car?

So he could take it out for a spin.

How do you spot a modern spider?

He doesn't have a web. He has a website.

Knock knock.
Who's there?
Lolli.
Lolli who?
Lollipop!

How does Om Nom greet a three-headed monster?

Hello, hello, hello!

What did Om Nom become after he was three days old?

Four days old.

What's green and goes up and down?

Om Nom in a lift.

What did the lamp say when Om Nom turned it off?

I'm delighted!

What's green, cute and has 16 wheels?

Om Nom on roller skates.

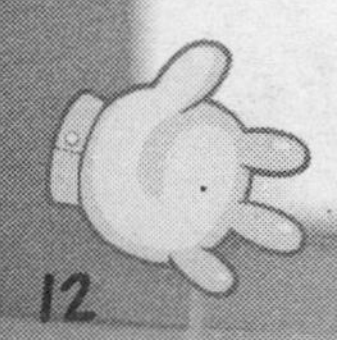

What is black, white, green and hungry?

Om Nom wearing a tuxedo.

What's the difference between Om Nom and a panther?

Om Nom is a green monster and panther what you wear.

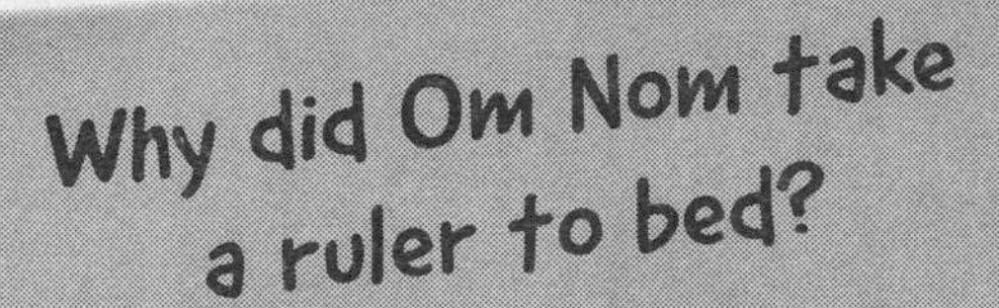

Why did Om Nom take a ruler to bed?

He wanted to measure how long he slept.

What sort of star is dangerous?

A shooting star.

What do you call a crazy star?

A lunar-tick.

What kind of candy do stars eat?

Flying saucers.

What do you call two spiders that just got married?
Newly webs.
Why did the fly fly?
Because the spider spied her.

Knock knock.

Who's there?

Lettuce.

Lettuce who?

Lettuce eat some more candy!

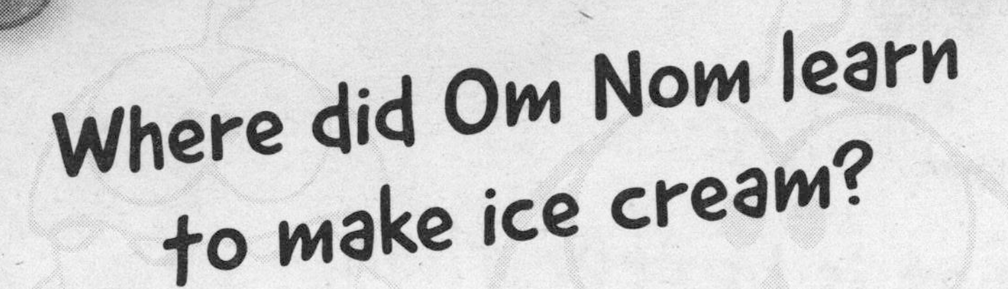

Where did Om Nom learn to make ice cream?

Sunday School.

What kind of tea does Om Nom like?

Sweeties.

Why does Om Nom's teacher wear sunglasses?

Because he is so bright.

What is better than a good friend?

A good friend with candy.

What do you get when you eat sweets on the beach?

Sandy candy.

Why did Om Nom take his doughnut to the dentist?

It needed a chocolate filling.

What's green and cute and jumps every 20 seconds?

Om Nom with hiccups!

Why won't Om Nom tell you the story of the blunt pencil?

He thinks it's pointless.

What does a spider do when he gets angry?

He goes up the wall.

What did the spider say when he broke his new web?

Darn it!

What do you call a spider that can lift an elephant over his head?

Sir!

Knock knock.

Who's there?

Justin.

Justin who?

Justin time for some candy!

Why did Om Nom paint himself purple?

So he could hide in the plum tree.

Why did Om Nom jump when he saw his school report?

It had a bee on it.

Why did the bee get married?

Because he found his honey!

How many pieces of rope would it take to reach the sun?

One. A very long one!

What's the biggest rope in the world?

Europe.

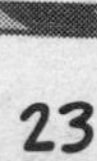

Why does Om Nom jump up and down before drinking his juice?

The carton said to 'shake well before drinking'.

What happened when Om Nom started to write poetry?

Things went from bad to verse.

What did the cat say
to Om Nom?

Meow.

Why did Om Nom tie his
face to a dog's tail?

He fancied a chinwag.

When is the best time of
year for Om Nom to bounce
on his trampoline?

Spring.

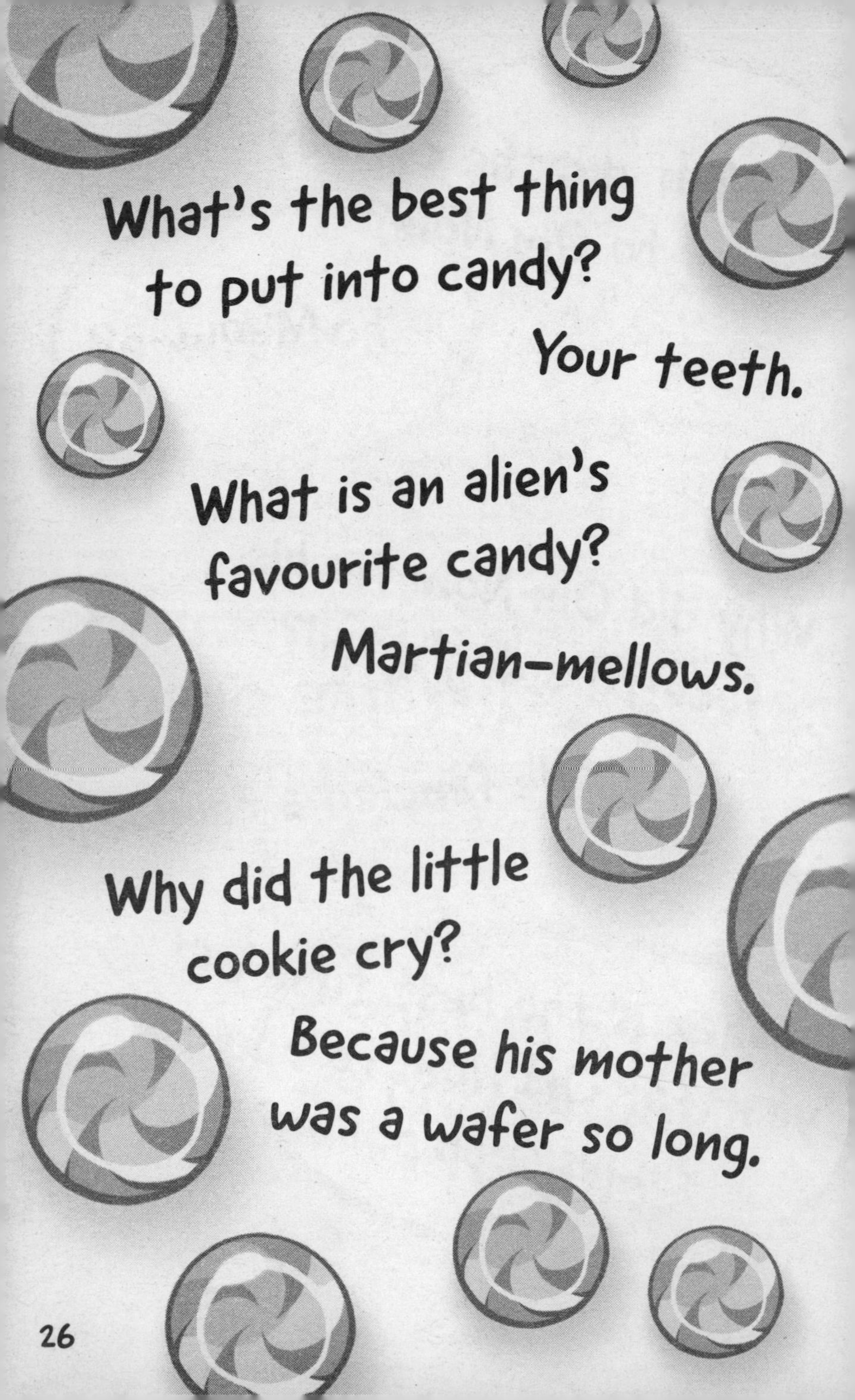

What's the best thing to put into candy?

Your teeth.

What is an alien's favourite candy?

Martian-mellows.

Why did the little cookie cry?

Because his mother was a wafer so long.

Knock knock.

Who's there?

White orange.

White orange who?

White orange you eating candy?

How does Om Nom say his ABCs backwards?

'CBA!'

What should you do if Om Nom eats your pen?

Use a pencil instead.

What's invisible and smells of candy?

Om Nom's breath.

Why does Om Nom keep his piano in the freezer?

Because he loves cool music.

What is the same size as Om Nom but weighs nothing?

Om Nom's shadow.

Why does Om Nom never believe anything spiders say?

Because they are always spinning him a yarn.

What do you call a hundred spiders on a tyre?

A spinning wheel.

What type of doctors are like spiders?

Spin doctors.

What did Om Nom say to his pencil?

You look sharp.

Why did Om Nom's school report get wet?

Because his grades were below 'C' level.

Knock knock.

Who's there?

Ida.

Ida who?

Ida love some candy!

Why did Om Nom throw his watch out the window?

He wanted to see time fly.

Why did Om Nom put a rabbit on his head?

Because he had no hare.

If Om Nom put seven cats in a box and one jumped out, how many are left?

None, they are all copycats.

What are spiders' webs good for?
Spiders.
How did the spider feel about going on stage?
He had butterflies in his stomach.

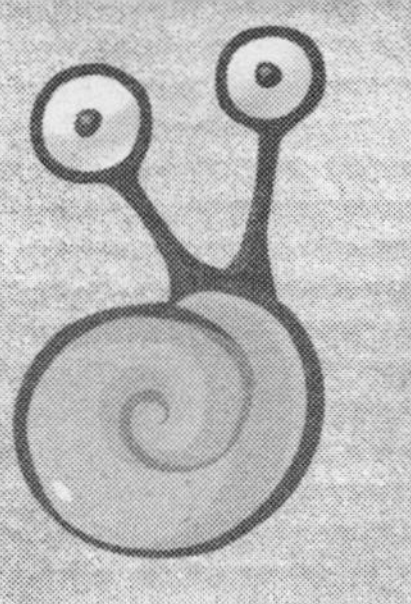

Why do spiders have eight legs?

So they can wrestle a fly while reading a newspaper.

What do you call a spider at the North Pole?

Lost.

Why is a snail the strongest animal?

He carries his house on his back.

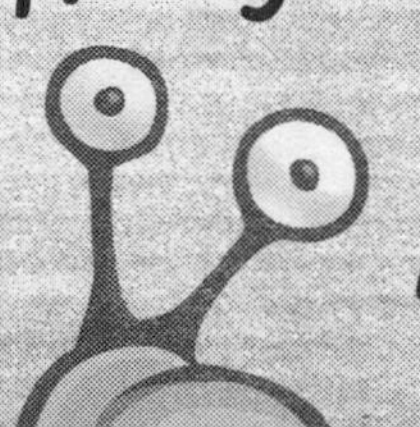

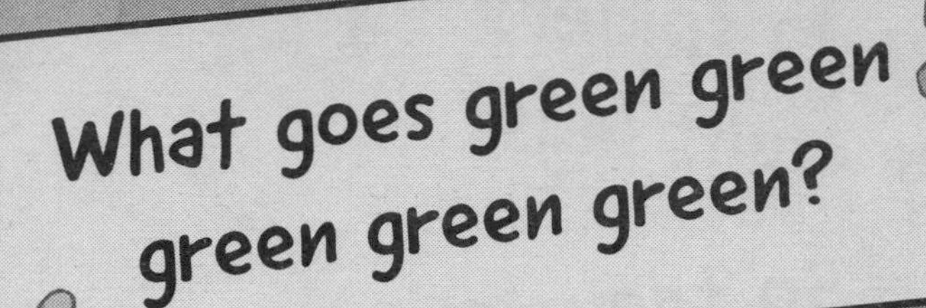

What goes green green green green green?

Om Nom rolling down a hill.

What happened when Om Nom hurt his funny bone?

He was in stitches for weeks.

Why does
Om Nom eat
very little candy?

Because big candy gets
stuck in his throat.

What did Om Nom get
when he crossed a poodle
with a chicken?

A cockapoodledoo.

What does Om Nom
do when it rains?

He gets wet.

Knock knock.

Who's there?

Dewey.

Dewey who?

Dewey have any candy for Om Nom?

Feed with Candy

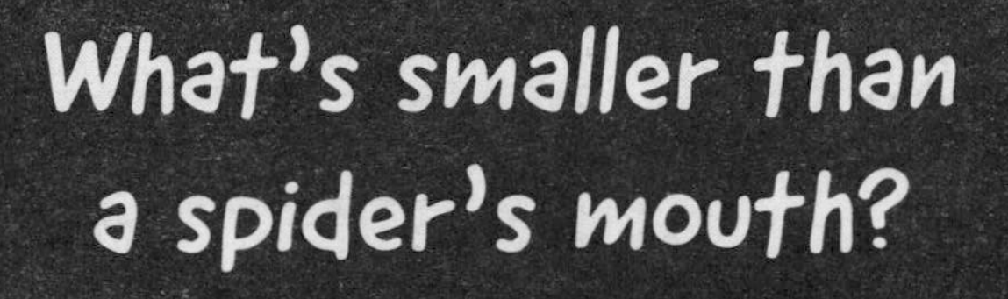

What's smaller than a spider's mouth?

A spider's dinner.

What do you get if you cross a rabbit with a spider?

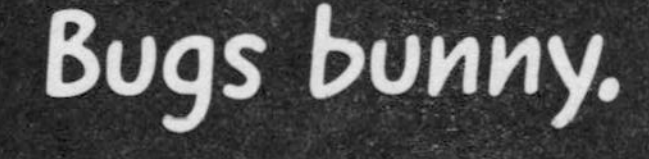

Bugs bunny.

Why did the spider fall off the rope?

He let go.

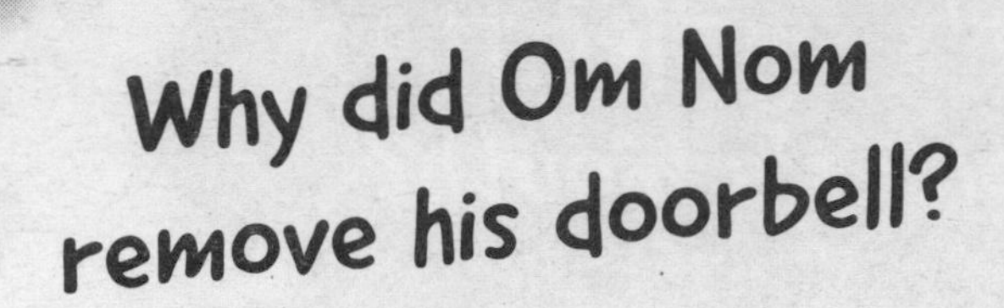

Why did Om Nom remove his doorbell?

He wanted to win a no-bell prize.

What do you call an elephant in Om Nom's box?

Stuck!

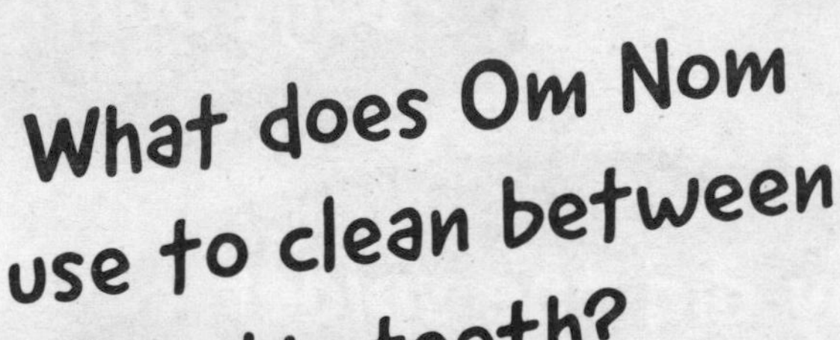

What does Om Nom use to clean between his teeth?

Candy floss.

What is Om Nom's favourite bird?

A swallow.

What happened when Om Nom slept under a car?

He woke up 'oily' the next morning.

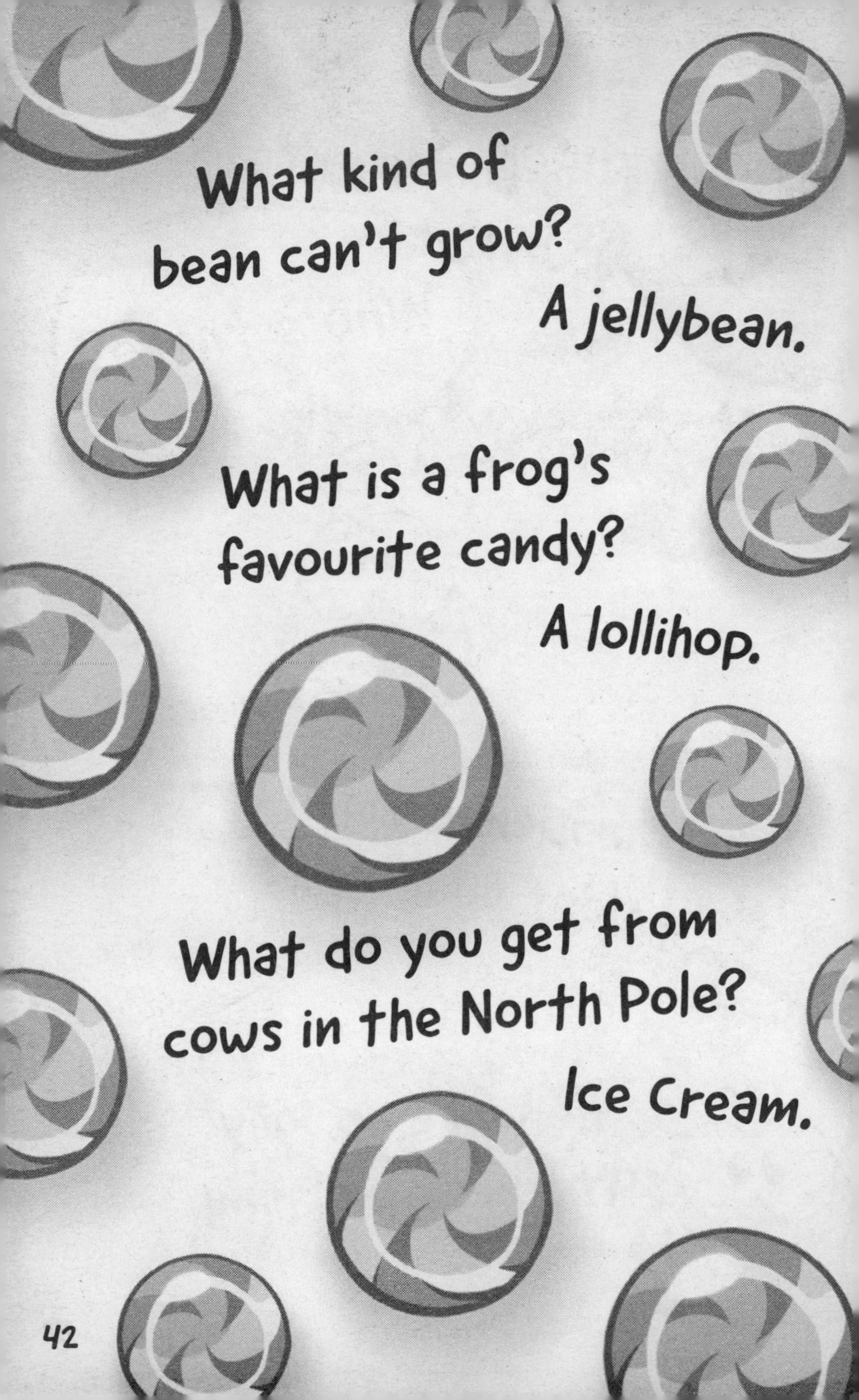

What kind of bean can't grow?

A jellybean.

What is a frog's favourite candy?

A lollihop.

What do you get from cows in the North Pole?

Ice Cream.

Knock knock.
Who's there?
Ken.
Ken who?
Ken you give Om Nom some candy please?

Doctor, Doctor
I swallowed a bone.

Are you choking?

No, I'm telling
the truth.

Doctor, Doctor, I just
swallowed a mouth organ.

Think yourself lucky you
don't play the piano.

Doctor, Doctor, every
time I drink hot chocolate I get a
pain in my eye.

Try taking the
spoon out first.

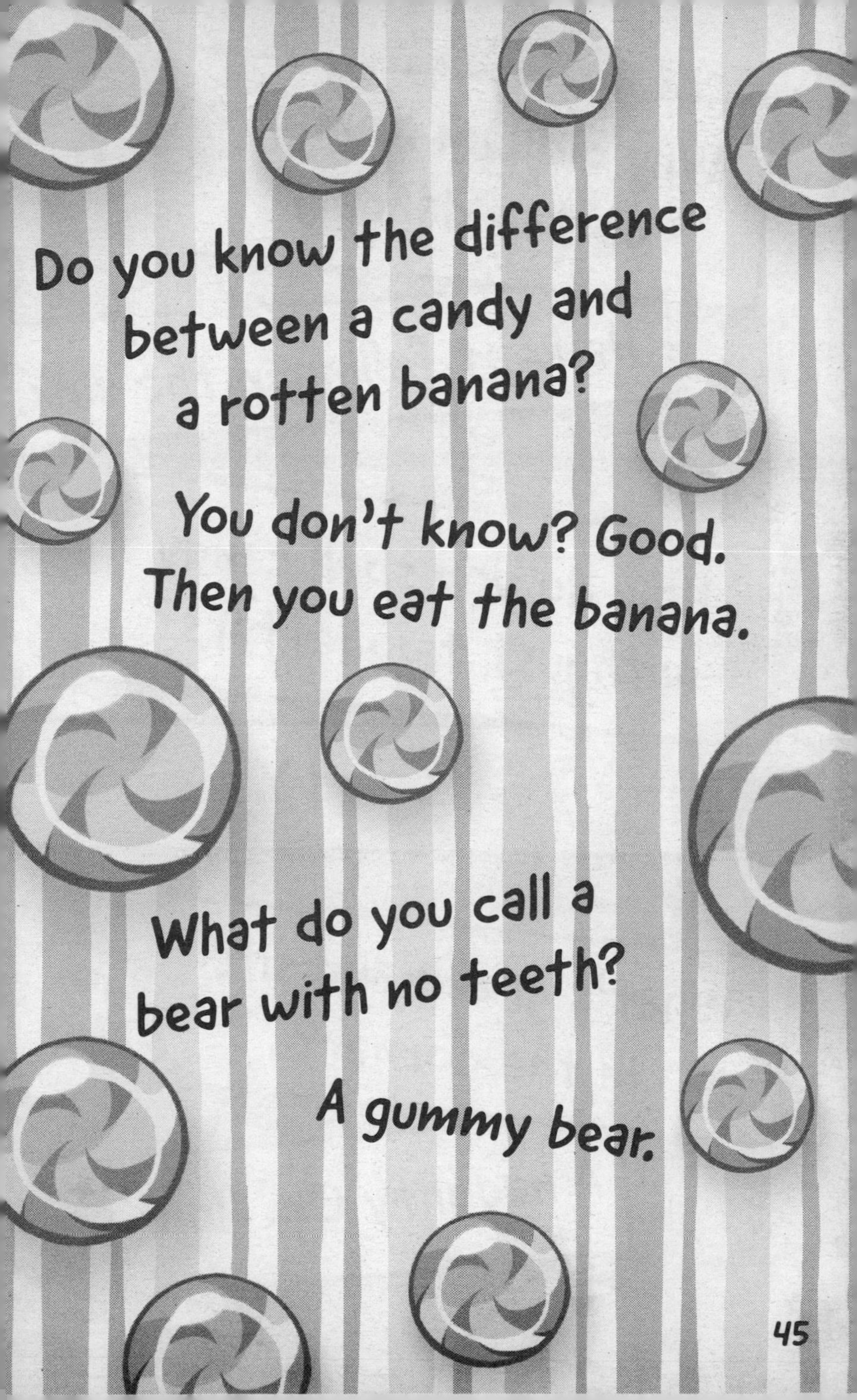

Do you know the difference between a candy and a rotten banana?

You don't know? Good. Then you eat the banana.

What do you call a bear with no teeth?

A gummy bear.

Why did Om Nom give up tap dancing?

He kept falling in the sink.

How do you spell candy with just two letters?

C and Y.

What's green and sits in the corner?

A naughty Om Nom.

Why did Om Nom swim across the ocean?

To get to the other tide.

How do you stop Om Nom digging up your garden?

Take his spade away.

What did one rope say to another?

That's knot mine.

When is a piece of rope not a piece of rope?

When it's a 'frayed knot'.

Why couldn't the rope answer the phone?

It was too tied up.

Knock knock.

Who's there?

Wooden shoe.

Wooden shoe who?

Wooden shoe like to eat some more candy?

Feed with Candy

How do you know if Om Nom is sleeping in your bed?

By the 'O' on his pyjamas.

Why was Om Nom standing on his head?

He was turning things over in his mind.

What's small, hungry and bright purple?

Om Nom holding his breath.

Why did Om Nom cross the road?

He was pretending to be a chicken.

Why does Om Nom think his teacher loves him?

She keeps putting red kisses on his work.

Why did Om Nom run from the kitchen when he was baking a cake?

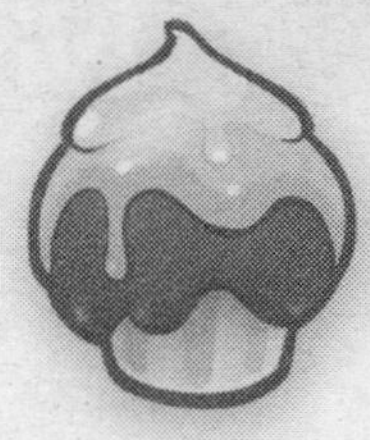

Because the recipe said crack an egg, then beat it.

Why did Om Nom wear boxing gloves to bed?

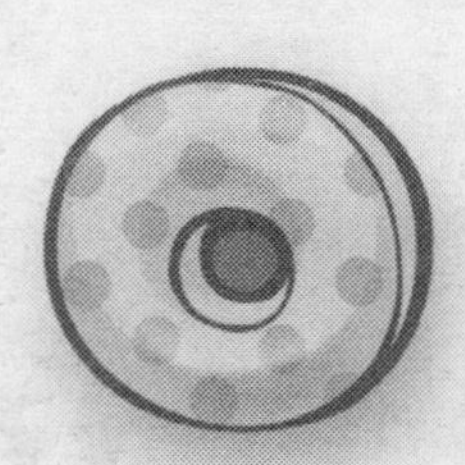

He wanted to hit the sack.

What did Om Nom get when he put three ducks in a box?

A box of quackers.

Why are spiders good to tease?
Because they have eight legs to pull.
What do spiders have that no other animal has?
Baby spiders.

Knock knock.

Who's there?

Canoe.

Canoe who?

Canoe give Om
Nom some candy.
He's hungry!

Why did Om Nom make friends with a snail?

He thought it needed to come out of its shell.

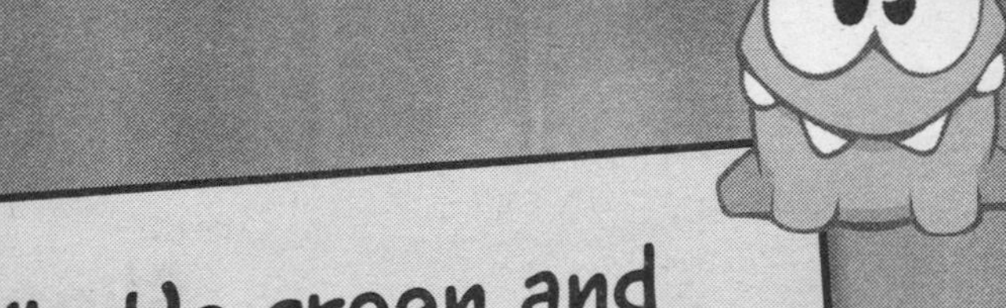

What's green and wears sunglasses?

Om Nom on holiday.

Why did Om Nom go out with a fig?

Because he couldn't find a date.

What does Om Nom call shoes made from bananas?

Slippers.

What did Om Nom get when he crossed a biscuit with a tuxedo?

A smart cookie.

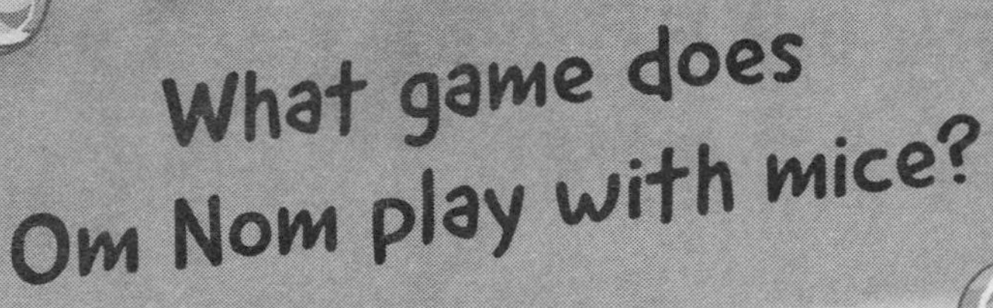

What game does Om Nom play with mice?

Hide and squeak.

How did Om Nom make the number one disappear?

He added a 'g' to it and then it was gone.

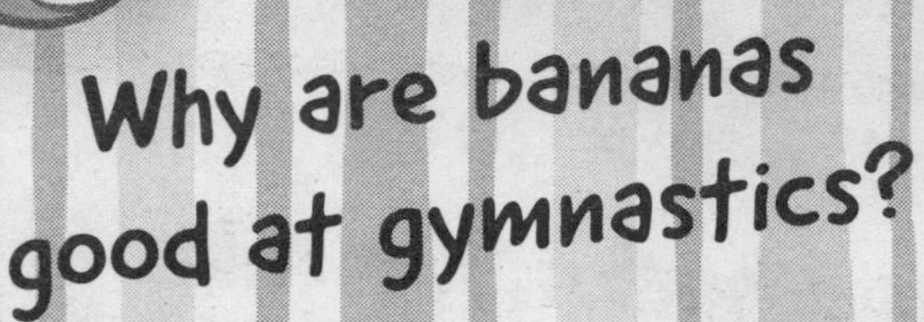

Why are bananas good at gymnastics?

They can always do the splits.

What did Om Nom think after eating the clown's candy?

'That tasted funny'.

What time is it when an elephant sits on your candy?

Time to buy some new candy.

Have you heard the joke about the jump rope?

Skip it.

Did you hear about the two ropes that had a race?

It ended in a tie.

Knock knock.

Who's there?

Howard.

Howard who?

Howard you like some more candy?

What is a spider's favourite month?

Web-uary.

What do you get if you cross a spider and an elephant?

I'm not sure, but if you see one walking across the ceiling then run before it collapses!

Why are spiders good swimmers?

They have webbed feet.

Why did Om Nom run around his bed?

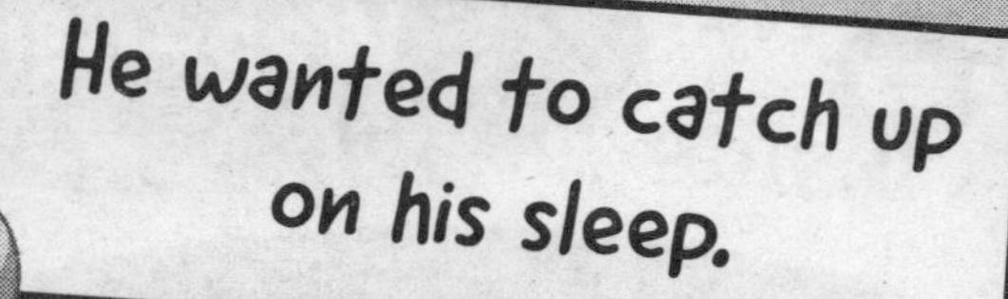

He wanted to catch up on his sleep.

Why did Om Nom take a pencil to bed?

He wanted to draw the curtains.

Why is Om Nom friends with a mushroom?

Because he is a fungi to be with.

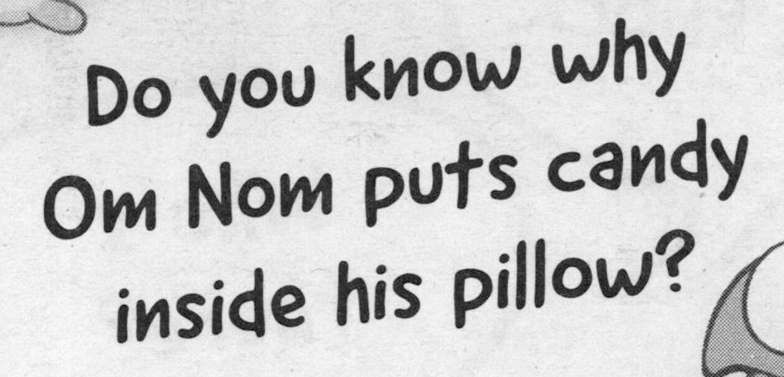

Do you know why Om Nom puts candy inside his pillow?

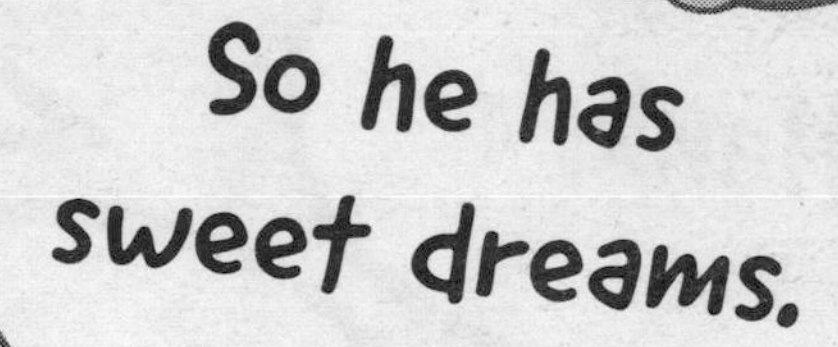

So he has sweet dreams.

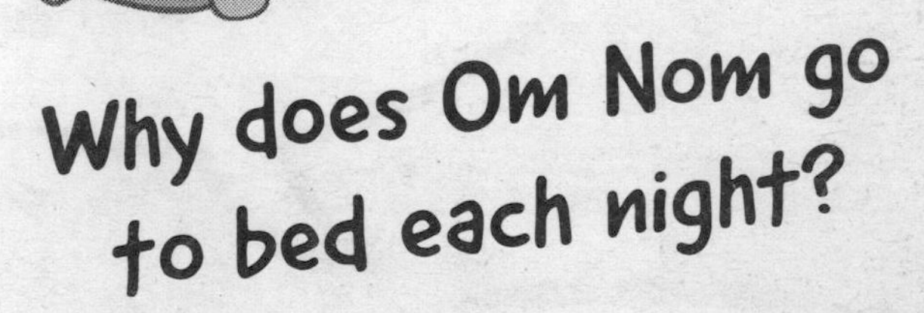

Why does Om Nom go to bed each night?

Because the bed won't come to him.

Knock knock.

Who's there?

Hank.

Hank who?

You're welcome!